Contents

Schofield &

Welcome to this book

Glossary

Section 1 Test 1

A WARM-UP

Write a sentence about computers.

1 In the past, _____

_____

2 Today, _____

_____

3 In the future, _____

_____

Underline the word that is **not** correct.

4 decide recent recult recite decent

5 difference space advice reverce reduce

Write the antonym.

6 inferior   _____

7 backhand   _____

8 minor   _____

9 exterior   _____

10 expansion   _____

B WORD WORK

1 Add the missing letters.

i e y

t h _ _ f   m _ s t _ r y

2 Write the plural forms of both words.

_____   _____

3 Add the suffix **er** or **or**.

perform____   invent____   report____

4 Describe the words you have created.

_____

_____

Write three more words of this type.

5 ending **er**: _____

6 ending **or**: _____

Write different definitions of each word.

7 **gear**: _____

_____

8 **gear**: _____

9 **coast** (verb): _____

10 **coast** (noun): _____

C SENTENCE WORK

Add a prepositional phrase.

1 _____, it was completely dark.

2 _____, it was completely dark.

3 _____, the man turned and spoke.

4 _____, the man turned and spoke.

Cross out the three main verbs or verb phrases. Improve the sentence by writing new and more powerful verbs.

5 The RSPCA asked people to help as it tried to cope with the crisis. _____

6 Residents left the meeting, saying that the situation had not been sorted.

_____

7 The wind blew through the trees, breaking branches and throwing them to the ground.

_____

Add punctuation and capital letters to these examples of direct speech.

8 Mrs Smith said It is very sad. We all feel let down

9 It's not fair Mick complained I want to go with you

10 Bill remembers the day well it was a bitterly cold morning he explains.

Section 1 Test 2

A WARM-UP

Continue the sentence.

1 He stayed with Jen until _____

2 He stayed with Jen as long as _____

_____

Make four words using these roots and affixes only.

trans port form er al

3 _____   5 _____

4 _____   6 _____

7 Add the same suffix to both words to make them into adjectives.

agree_____   charge_____

8 Add a different prefix to each of the words you have made. Write the new words.

_____

Change one letter to make another onomatopoeia. Write the new word.

9 **chatter**   _____

10 **plod**   _____

B WORD WORK

Underline the word that is spelt correctly.

1 identifyed identifying

2 carryer carrying

3 marrying marryage

4 worryer worrying

5 Write the correct spelling of the words that were wrongly spelt.

_____

6 Add the correct '**shun**' ending.

techni_____   comple_____

posses_____   conclu_____

7 What kind of words have you made by adding the suffixes? Underline the correct answer.

verbs nouns adjectives

Write two more formal synonyms of the words in **bold**.

8 I'm **whacked**.   _____

9 It's a **phoney**.   _____

10 We must **come clean**. _____

C SENTENCE WORK

Use one of these words to combine the two sentences. **that where who**

1 A theatre is a public building. Plays are performed there.

_____

2 An orchestra is a group of musicians. They play many kinds of instruments.

_____

3 A thermostat is a device on a heater. It controls the temperature.

_____

Underline the adverb and explain why the writer has used it.

4 She answered wearily. _____

5 He is very clever. _____

6 Unfortunately, City won 2–0. _____

Complete the phrase by writing in an item or items belonging to the characters. Use the correct punctuation.

7 the pirates_____

8 the witches_____

9 the gang_____

10 the sheep_____

Section 1 Test 3

A WARM-UP

Continue the sentence with a prepositional phrase.

1 Gus was left there _____

_____

2 Gus was left there _____

_____

3 Gus was left there _____

_____

4 Continue the sentence using a conjunction.

Gus was left there _____

_____

Add the same root to all three words.

5 _____ son   _____ corn   _____ cycle

6 _____ ury   _____ igrade   _____ ipede

7 _____ nova   _____ highway   _____ power

Put the letters in order to make a word.

8 g a r e l   _____

9 e r u s   _____

10 l e t s y   _____

B WORD WORK

The same syllable is missing from both words. Write it in.

1 wid____ing   threat____ing

2 eas____ly   laz____ly

3 con____ence   re____ence

Split the word to show the root word and affixes.

4 overtaking   _____ / _____ / _____

5 regeneration   _____ / _____ / _____

6 unbeneficial   _____ / _____ / _____

Add a prefix and a suffix to make a new word.

7 _____control_____

8 _____connect_____

Write in full the words that the letters stand for.

9 HQ   _____

10 ROM   _____

C SENTENCE WORK

Embed the information from the second sentence into the first. Write the new sentence.

1 Michael helped David to escape. Michael is David's brother.

_____

2 Mrs Simmons raised £1000 for the charity. She works in a bank.

_____

3 Ben won first prize. He is aged sixteen.   _____

Sort the adjectives into two groups.   **calm cold rash sincere conceited fearless**

4 **positive:** _____   **5** **negative:** _____

Cross out the words that sound negative. Write new words that are more positive.

6 Peculiar house for sale: cramped rooms and lots of old features.   _____

7 Lucy was so nosy, with her prying eyes and constant smirk.   _____

Add the missing full stops, commas and capital letters.

8 Aaron ran down the hill shouting loudly the dog ignoring me bounded after him.

9 After two difficult years Marie then aged ten went to live with her grandmother.

10 The strangers came to a halt Jessica looked up pale and frightened.

X There is only one correct answer.   X There is more than one correct answer.

Section 1 Test 4

A WARM-UP

Write two adverbs which would show that a character is

1 sad: _____

2 happy: _____

3 scared: _____

Add the missing root.

Clue: to do with computers

4 _____active

5 _____link

6 _____media

7 Write one other word with each root.

_____

Underline the odd one out.

8 **possessive pronouns:** ours its his there's

9 **prepositions:** with at during an

10 **conjunctions:** but if all until

B WORD WORK

Add each suffix and write the new words.

ing ed ment

1 move _____

2 involve _____

3 What spelling rule did you use?

_____

_____

Add one more word to each set.

4 predict prehistoric _____

5 exit exclude _____

6 Write the meaning of the prefix.

pre: _____   ex: _____

Write four different definitions.

7 beat: _____

8 beat: _____

9 beat: _____

10 beat: _____

C SENTENCE WORK

Describe the technique that the writer has used in the title.

1 **The Loch Ness monster – does it exist?** _____

2 **Save the whale – NOW!** _____

3 **A simple solution?** _____

4 Use one of these techniques to write the title of an article on solar power.

_____

Rewrite the sentence so that it sounds less definite.

5 The ground will be ready on time. _____

6 In the future we will all have electric cars. _____

7 Michael used the key to escape. _____

8 Rewrite this line from a playscript, using the correct punctuation and capital letters.

Olivia anxiously did you find it _____

9 Rewrite the line as direct speech. _____

10 Rewrite the line as reported speech. _____

X There is only one correct answer.   X There is more than one correct answer.

7

Section 1　Test 5

A　WARM-UP

Use the words **cat** and **bowl** in

1 **a sentence:** _____

_____

2 **an imperative:** _____

_____

3 **a question:** _____

_____

4 **a rhyming couplet:**

_____

_____

weary polite tidy

Add the same suffix to each of the three words to make

5 **nouns:** _____

6 **adverbs:** _____

7 **superlatives:** _____

Write a word using these letters. The letters must be used in this order.

8 **r t n**　_____

9 **d b l**　_____

10 **p f m**　_____

B　WORD WORK

1 Add **ie** or **ei**.

p___c e　　b r___f l y　　r e c___p t

2 What rule did you use?

_____

3 What do you notice about the spelling of these words?

weigh neigh eight height

_____

4 Write the word that sounds like the odd one out.

_____

Write three words related to the word in **bold**.

5 **hero**　_____

6 **just**　_____

7 **know**　_____

Write a definition. **Clue: to do with plants**

8 **germination:** _____

9 **dispersal:** _____

10 **pollination:** _____

C　SENTENCE WORK

Identify the text type.

1 The brave teenager, now resting at home, rescued her trapped friends.　_____

2 Hundreds of homeless animals are in urgent need of your help – right now.　_____

3 The man with the white beard stood in the quiet, moonlit square.　_____

Give two ways in which the nouns in sentences 1 to 3 are modified.

4 _____　　5 _____

Write four words that could be used to complete the sentence.

6 He _____ be late today.　　_____

7 They _____ have passed us.　　_____

8 Put a tick if the apostrophes are used correctly. Put a cross if they are not.

Jenny's mum hadn't any money.　____　　Fan's were eager to see Citys' new signing.　____

We could'nt hear the actor's dialogue.　____

Write correctly the sentences that you have put a cross beside.

9 _____

10 _____

8　
　X　There is only one correct answer.　　X　There is more than one correct answer.

Section 1   Test 6

A   WARM-UP

Write an advertising slogan for a new snack called choco-pops. Use

1 **rhyme:** _____

_____

2 **alliteration:** _____

_____

3 **word play:** _____

_____

4 **simile:** _____

_____

What word could you write in the gap to make a new word? Write two possibilities.

5 dis_____ ly   _____

6 un_____ able   _____

7 im _____ ion   _____

Add the name of a drink to complete the word.

8 _____ s e

9 _____ n d e r

10 _____ u l a r

B   WORD WORK

Cross out the words that are wrongly spelt. Write the correct spelling.

1 To my releif, the queshuns were not difercult.

_____

2 The worter looked inviteing, she thourt.

_____

Add two words with the same ending.

3 **quarrelsome** _____

4 **toward** _____

5 **lengthwise** _____

Draw a line to join the ending to its meaning.

6 **some**   in that way

7 **ward**   full of that quality

8 **wise**   in the given direction

Underline the words that

9 can be **nouns** as well as **adjectives:**

ugly annual large final busy

10 can be **nouns** as well as **verbs:**

cook rely polish deliver compose

C   SENTENCE WORK

Reorder the words to make three different sentences that sound better than the single sentence given.

The King saw the statue unfortunately as he entered the castle in the evening.

1 _____

2 _____

3 _____

She walked.

Write two adverbs or adverbial phrases that could be added to the sentence to say

4 **how:** _____

5 **where:** _____

6 **when:** _____

Add a pair of brackets within each sentence.

7 Some eagles build their nests called eyries on cliff tops.

8 Ned kept the two dogs Shep and Flick for many years.

9 Rob Jones the team's manager was unhappy with the decision.

10 What other punctuation could have been used instead of brackets? _____

Section 1   Test 7

A   WARM-UP

Write a sentence using these words.
football cake

1 **simple sentence:** _____

_____

2 **complex sentence:** _____

_____

3 Draw a line to join the root to the suffix.

auto	ic
therm	mate
phon	ference
circum	al

Write the meaning of the root.

4 **auto:** _____   **6** **phon:** _____

5 **therm:** _____   **7** **circum:** _____

All these compound words are to do with computers.
Complete them

8 **using adjectives:** _____ cut _____ ware

9 **using prepositions:** _____ load _____ line

10 **using nouns:** _____ bar _____ work

B   WORD WORK

1 Underline the root words.

dangerous prosperous offering

2 Write each word split into syllables.

_____ / _____ / _____   _____ / _____ / _____

_____ / _____ / _____

3 Which letter is unstressed in all these words?

_____

Write the word to go with the definition.
*Clue: starts with **in** or **im***

4 _____ : cannot be seen

5 _____ : unfinished

6 _____ : childish

7 _____ : fixed, cannot be moved

8 _____ : faulty, flawed

9 _____ : wrong, not exact

10 Write the longer word that each word comes from.

fridge _____

panto _____

flu _____

intercom _____

C   SENTENCE WORK

Underline the main clause.

1 He waited for hours despite the rain.   **2** I enjoyed the game even though we lost.

Rewrite 1 and 2 above with the subordinate clause at the start.

3 _____   **4** _____

Extend and improve the sentence to match the story genre.

5 A man went down the street. (fantasy)

_____

6 She heard footsteps. (traditional tale)

_____

7 He saw a face. (horror)

_____

Add a colon and continue the sentence.

8 An imperative is a command. For example _____

9 Abby checked her pockets _____

10 For this trick you need a few simple objects _____

X There is only one correct answer.   X There is more than one correct answer.

Section 1   Test 8

A   WARM-UP

Read the headline. Then write the first sentence of the article.

1   **United on cloud nine** _____

_____

_____

2   **Thief caught red-handed** _____

_____

_____

Write two words related to the word in **bold**.

3   **apology**   _____

4   **mystery**   _____

5   **apply**   _____

6   **calculate**   _____

7   Make six words using these roots and affixes only.

act view inter re er

_____

_____

Add a short word to complete the longer word.

8   mea_____ment   **10**   ac_____ingly

9   disap_____ed

B   WORD WORK

Add suffixes to each root word to make three new words.

ing ed age er or able

1   stop_____   stop_____   stop_____

2   plan_____   plan_____   plan_____

3   edit_____   edit_____   edit_____

4   Which root word is unusual?

_____

_____

Add the correct prefix.

5   The footballer signed a new _____tract.

6   I can _____tract him while you escape.

7   Nothing will _____tract from her success.

Write a definition.

8   **pitch** (in music): _____

9   **pitch** (in sport): _____

10   **pitch** (in camping): _____

C   SENTENCE WORK

Link the sentences in four different ways. You can change the order if you want to.

It was still snowing. Amy rushed outside. She made a snowman.

1   _____

2   _____

3   _____

4   _____

Write three alternatives for the word in **bold**. They do not have to be synonyms.

5   The man was **very** old.   _____

6   The dog was **on** the table.   _____

7   Write the name of the class of words that you used

in 5: _____   in 6: _____

Where might you use speech marks in a text of this type?

8   **in a newspaper report:** _____

9   **in a biography:** _____

10   **in a book review:** _____

Section 1   Test 9

A   WARM-UP

Reorder the words to make three different sentences.

was Stanley sitting there beside her

1 _____

2 _____

3 _____

Underline the possessive pronoun that is hidden in each word.

4 determined   **5** profits

Underline the preposition that is hidden in each word.

6 money   **7** recovery

Write an adverb using the word in **bold**.

8 **heart** _____

9 **fury** _____

10 Underline the word to which you can add **all** these prefixes.

re im dis

claim cover prove press

B   WORD WORK

Add the missing syllables.

1 _____ / ven /_____

Clue: exciting journey or series of events

2 ap / _____ / hen / _____

Clue: anxious

3 des / _____ / na / _____

Clue: where you are going to

4 _____ / lu /_____ /_____

Clue: light up

Write two words related to the word in **bold**.

5 **create** _____

6 **vary** _____

7 **image** _____

Write a definition.
Clue: found in a book about the Moon

8 **weightlessness:** _____

9 **uninhabitable:** _____

10 **spherical:** _____

C   SENTENCE WORK

Add the missing full stops, commas and capital letters.

1 Simon turned it was the same voice yes there was the mysterious stranger

2 There was a crash Stella jumped she clutched the chair waiting

3 Underline the word that best describes how the text made you feel

in 1: excited calm scared   **in 2:** thrilled calm tense

4 How did the punctuation help create these effects? _____

Write three connectives or connective phrases that could be used

5 **to show a result:** _____

6 **to add more information:** _____

7 **to oppose:** _____

Continue the sentence with a simile or a metaphor that creates a feeling of

8 **panic:** The crowd _____

9 **calm:** The wind _____

10 **excitement:** The acrobat _____

X There is only one correct answer.   X There is more than one correct answer.

Section 1   Test 10

A   WARM-UP

They found that the Tardis had disappeared.

Rewrite this sentence as

1 an exclamation: _____

_____

2 a question: _____

_____

_____

3 a complex sentence: _____

_____

_____

The ending of the word is missing. Write two suggestions as to what the complete word might be.

4 illu _____ _____

5 imm _____ _____

6 intr _____ _____

Write two words related to the word in **bold**.

7 **perform** _____

8 **drama** _____

9 **idea** _____

10 **assist** _____

B   WORD WORK

Add the same ending to all three words.

ery ary ory

1 diction_____   prim_____   ordin_____

2 flatt_____   lott_____   machin_____

3 categ_____   fact_____   hist_____

4 Make four words using these roots and suffixes only.

graph auto bio y logy

_____

_____

Write the meaning of the root.

5 **auto:** _____   **7** **bio:** _____

6 **graph:** _____   **8** **logy:** _____

9 Write a definition.

motel: _____

brunch: _____

fanzine: _____

10 How were all the words created?

_____

C   SENTENCE WORK

Add a subordinate clause that gives a contrasting idea.

1 Some believe that the fire was caused deliberately _____

2 Hannah was trembling _____

3 They continued to struggle _____

4 City had the better first half, _____

The subject is **Forest fires**. Write sentences on this subject for each of these text types.

5 a newspaper report: _____

6 an explanation: _____

7 an imaginative description: _____

Add the missing apostrophes.

8 At six oclock were off to Jacks to watch Citys replay.

9 Im worried cause I dont think Ill be able to go to Mareks party.

10 Its Annies idea but she says it wont work without my parents help.

Section 1 Test 11

A WARM-UP

1 Write a complex sentence using these words.

book hair pencil

_____

_____

Write four words with the ending **ture**.

First write two two-syllable words.

2 _____ **3** _____

Now write two three-syllable words.

4 _____ **5** _____

Write two suffixes that you could add to all the words.

sharp tight bright deep light

6 ____ **7** ____

Complete the simile.

8 As springy as _____

9 As welcome as _____

10 As silent as _____

B WORD WORK

Add the missing vowels.

1 l _ m _ n _ d e

2 s _ m _ l _ r

3 s k _ l _ t _ n

4 b _ n _ f _ t

Write a noun related to the word in **bold**.

5 survive   _____

6 science   _____

Write an adjective related to the word in **bold**.

7 courage   _____

8 construct   _____

These words are in a novel set in Victorian times. What do they mean?

9 victuals: _____

10 comforter: _____

C SENTENCE WORK

Is the sentence active or passive? Write your answer.

1 The case was closed.   _____

2 A stranger opened the door.   _____

3 Rain destroyed the crops.   _____

Rewrite the active sentences as passive sentences.

4 _____   **5** _____

Continue the sentence so that it builds up suspense.

6 I followed the path _____

_____

Write two short contrasting sentences to follow the long complex one that you have just written.

7 _____   **8** _____

Punctuate the extract.

9 Mr Gold remembers Ilford as it was My aunts flat was above Wilsons dairy he recalls

10 Julia Hopkins who judged the competition said Nikkis poster is really eye catching

X There is only one correct answer. X There is more than one correct answer.

Section 1   Test 12

A   WARM-UP

Write a pun based on the homophones.

1   hair/hare: _____

_____

2   right/write: _____

_____

3   sent/scent: _____

_____

4   you/ewe: _____

_____

Underline the words that

5   do not have a plural form:

child furniture goose advice

6   do not have a singular form:

trousers wolves binoculars teeth

7   are the same whether singular or plural:

sheep mice patio deer solo

Add the same prefix to all three words.

8   ____fault   ____flate   ____compose

9   ____exist   ____operate   ____-star

10   ____large   ____grave   ____trust

B   WORD WORK

Cross out the words that are wrongly spelt.
Write the correct spelling.

1   consernant: a letter of the alfabet that

is not a vowle _____

2   ajective: a werd that discribes a known

_____

3   simele: when a writter makes a comperison

_____

Write the root word and its meaning.

4   popular population populate

_____ means _____

5   pedal pedestrian pedometer

_____ means _____

6   aeroplane aerospace aerosol

_____ means _____

7   prime primary primrose

_____ means _____

Write two synonyms.

8   also _____

9   so _____

10   next _____

C   SENTENCE WORK

Rewrite the sentence in the passive form.

1   City won the game. _____

2   The Mayor presented the prize. _____

3   Jaguar made the car in 1922. _____

4   The waves splashed the spectators. _____

The old lady glared at the boy standing by her gate.

5   Is the sentence in the first, second or third person? _____

Rewrite and add more detail to the sentence from the point of view of

6   the woman: _____

7   the boy: _____

Punctuate the sentence so that it sounds effective.

8   They had no key and yet as if by magic slowly so very slowly the door opened

9   Try them today they're great

10   What different effects have been created in these two sentences?

_____

Now complete Section 1 of the Progress chart on page 46.   **15**

Section 1 Writing task: The happening

Task

Read the first line of the story, as given in the box below. Write the next part of the story.

Hints

Before you start:

- Decide on the genre or type of your story. For example, it could be a fantasy, adventure or realistic story.
- Think about the main character. Who is David, and are any other characters involved?
- Decide on the story setting.
- Plan the events in your story: what has happened and why, and what does David do next? Work out the sequence of events.
- Consider whether there are other vital details that should be included.

As you write:

- Think about your audience and how to tell the story effectively.
- Think carefully as you choose your words and story-telling techniques.

David woke up. He knew immediately that something strange had happened.

Continue on a separate sheet.

Check

- When you have finished, check through your story.
- Edit and proofread it.
- Make sure that everything looks and sounds right.

Section 1 Proofreading task: Flood!

Task

Proofread this radio news report.

Hints

- Check that everything is clear and sounds right.
- Check the punctuation.
- Check the spelling.
- Change anything that does not look or sound right.

All day worter levuls have continewed to rise threatning many locul home's.

Mr Jackson the cheef flood offiser said of coarse people are feeling apprahensive and we are offring addvise and asistence wearever posserble.

The floods have allso coursed caos for trannsport earlyer on the polise said that "it was dangrus to travul and peeple shoud stay put as many drivers cars was allready underworter."

The Brown famerly who live in the villije told us "they could not beleive how quickerly the warter rows but they were releeved to be safe."

It seems peeple have no worning of the danjer, even thowgh their is a histery of flooding in the locall erea.

Wether forcastor's are pradictting more rain this everning so it is posserble that there is werse to come.

Extra

Imagine that you are to present a radio news report about a hurricane that hit your area last night. On a separate sheet of paper, write the beginning of your report.

Section 2   Test 1

A   WARM-UP

Rewrite the sentence, replacing some of the words with more interesting ones.

1 The woman gets out of the car.

_____

_____

2 The dog looked at the man.

_____

_____

3 The man came into the room.

_____

_____

Add one letter to make a new word.

4 **smile** _____

5 **cause** _____

6 **phase** _____

7 **nun** _____

Write two words related to the word in **bold**.

8 **destroy** _____

9 **apply** _____

10 **equal** _____

B   WORD WORK

Part of each word is missing. Write in some letters to make a complete word.

1 script_____   _____script_____   _____script

2 verb_____   _____verb   _____verb

3 part_____   _____part_____   _____part

Underline the correct spelling.

4 terrifyied terrified terrifyed

5 hurryedly hurridly hurriedly

6 fancyful fanciful fancifull

7 sunniest sunnyest suniest

Write a definition of the word in **bold**.

8 the sea **bed**: _____

_____

9 at the **crease**: _____

_____

10 a **litter** of three: _____

_____

C   SENTENCE WORK

Rewrite the information as a single complex sentence. Do so in two different ways.

Oxygen is a gas. It is found in the air. It is essential to life.

1 _____

2 _____

3 Why do the complex sentences sound better? _____

Add a **prepositional phrase** to modify the noun and an **adverb** to modify the verb or adjective.

4 The cat _____ sat _____ outside.

5 The man _____ was not _____ amused.

6 The tree _____ was swaying _____ .

One day almost five years later the man returned.

Punctuate the sentence using

7 **commas:** _____

8 **brackets:** _____

9 **dashes:** _____

10 What are the different effects of these punctuation marks? _____

_____

18   ⊠ There is only one correct answer.   ⊠ There is more than one correct answer.

Section 2 Test 2

A WARM-UP

Add three adverbs to make a sentence that says **when**, **how** and **where**.

1 _____ it rained

  _____ .

2 _____ we played

  _____ .

3 The man _____

  waits _____ .

Make a word that ends and a word that starts with each letter string.

4 _____ ex → ex_____

5 _____ cy → cy_____

6 _____ ce → ce_____

Write a sentence using the homophones.

7 **bear/bare:** _____

8 **whale/wail:** _____

9 **dear/deer:** _____

10 **hare/hair:** _____

B WORD WORK

Add a suffix to make the word into a noun.

1 suspend_____

2 alter_____

Write a noun related to the word in **bold**.
It should describe a person who

3 **tours:** _____

4 **assists:** _____

Add the missing syllables.

5 im / _____ / _____ / _____ / ly
  Clue: straightaway

6 ap / _____ / _____ / _____ / ly
  Clue: roughly, about

7 ex / _____ / _____ / _____ / ary
  Clue: remarkable

Write a modern word or phrase that means the same.

8 **wireless:** _____

9 **primer:** _____

10 **automobile:** _____

C SENTENCE WORK

Complete the sentence using these words. **orange football**

1 Although _____

2 After _____

3 As _____

4 Draw a ring round the main clause in each sentence.

You are writing an advert for a new brand of trainers. Write three techniques you might use, giving an example of each one.

5 _____   _____

6 _____   _____

7 _____   _____

Add two commas.

8 They plunged onwards pushing deeper into the tunnel losing all sense of direction.

9 Meanwhile, Sophie sitting on the hillside felt the land tremble beneath her.

10 Apes unlike monkeys have no tails.

Section 2   Test 3

A   WARM-UP

Write a sentence using these words.

pigeon   wall

1 simple sentence: _____

_____

2 compound sentence: _____

_____

3 complex sentence: _____

_____

Complete the mnemonic, which helps you to spell the word in **bold**.

4 You find a _____ in an **acci** _____ .

5 There is a _____ in **sepa** _____ e.

6 Poor old _____ is in **hospit** _____ .

7 Find the **p** _____ in **p** _____ ces.

Write two words related to the word in **bold**.

8 identity _____

9 belief _____

10 human _____

B   WORD WORK

Write the word to go with the definition.
The word begins with one of these prefixes.

il im ir

1 _____ : will never die

2 _____ : against the law

3 _____ : cannot be changed back
or undone

Add **ei** or **ie** to make the long **ee** sound.

4   d e c ___ t   y ___ l d   s ___ z e

5   r e l ___ v e   s ___ g e   w ___ r d

6 Which two words in questions 4 and 5 do **not** follow the normal 'i before e' rule?

_____

Complete the well-known saying.

7 All that glitters _____

8 The early bird _____

9 There's no smoke _____

10 Honesty is _____

C   SENTENCE WORK

Complete the sentence so that it follows this one.

Rays from the sun can be harmful.

1 For example, _____

2 Furthermore, _____

3 Therefore, _____

4 However, _____

Change the verb to include either **have** or **has**.

5 We ~~are holding~~ _____ talks with the shop's owner.

6 The plants ~~are beginning~~ _____ to grow.

7 The wind ~~is doing~~ _____ a lot of damage.

8 Miss Hawkins ~~is teaching~~ _____ us about plants.

Add three more items to the list.

9 The room was full of treasure: necklaces of glistening stones; rings with _____

_____

10 He created a sumptuous feast: plates of roasted meats; steaming _____

_____

X There is only one correct answer.   X There is more than one correct answer.

Section 2 Test 4

A WARM-UP

Rewrite the sentence, changing the word order as you do so.

A figure appeared slowly, as the mist faded.

1 _____

_____

2 _____

_____

3 _____

_____

Write a word using these letters. The letters must be used in this order.

4 **i l n** _____

5 **a f d** _____

6 **x p n** _____

Add the missing animal.

7 Like water off a _____ back.

8 Let the _____ out of the bag.

9 Give a _____ a bad name.

10 Like a _____ out of water.

B WORD WORK

Write sentences to show three different meanings of the word **just**.

1 _____

2 _____

3 _____

4 Make four words by adding these affixes to the word **just**. Use each affix once only.

ad un in able ice ly ify

_____

The same letter string is missing from all three words. Write it in.

5 offi_____   spe_____   benefi_____

6 vill_____   mess_____   dam_____

7 import_____   eleph_____   const_____

8 do_____   ba_____   bu_____

Write three words that end like this.

9 **clude:** _____

10 **gram:** _____

C SENTENCE WORK

Rewrite the sentence in the passive form.

1 A security man guarded the painting. _____

2 Dr Gill organised the competition. _____

3 The mud ruined her shoes. _____

4 The Emperor saved the kingdom. _____

5 How is the passive version different? _____

Continue the sentence to create different moods.

6 The room _____

7 The room _____

Punctuate the sentences. Use different punctuation marks in each one.

8 It seemed to me or perhaps I imagined it that the old man smiled.

9 If she fails as I think she will we must go on alone.

10 The planets orbit travel round the Sun.

Section 2 Test 5

A WARM-UP

Use the words **car** and **tree** in

1 an imperative: _____

_____

2 a passive sentence: _____

_____

3 a complex sentence: _____

_____

4 a rhyming couplet: _____

_____

_____

Make a word that ends and a word that starts
with each letter string.

5 _____ ves ➔ ves _____

6 _____ phy ➔ phy _____

7 _____ que ➔ que _____

Underline the correct spelling.

8 busyest busiest busyist bussiest

9 lonelier lonlier lonelyer lonelyier

10 worryedly worridly worriedly worriedley

B WORD WORK

1 Add the correct prefix.

post pre

_____ caution _____ script _____ view

Write the meaning of the prefix.

2 pre: _____ **3** post: _____

Add **able** or **ible**.

4 vis _____ detest _____ resist _____

5 formid _____ accept _____ aud _____

Which two words above do **not** follow the usual
able/ible pattern?

6 _____ **7** _____

8 What is the normal rule for adding **able**
and **ible**?

_____

_____

Write a definition of the well-known saying.

9 **in the limelight:** _____

10 **to be given the sack:** _____

C SENTENCE WORK

Ravi waited by the door.

Rewrite the sentence, adding a subordinate clause to the

1 beginning: _____

2 middle: _____

3 end: _____

Write the text type that each sentence is taken from.

4 Mr Johal was born in 1948 in King's Norton, Birmingham. _____

5 I was born in Hastings but my family moved to London when I was just two. _____

6 Have just got in from college. What a day! _____

7 Which is the most informal? _____ Which is the most impersonal? _____

Add a colon and complete the sentence.

8 He read the words on the sign _____

9 Here is the address you need _____

10 Evie read the opening words _____

22 |x| There is only one correct answer. |x| There is more than one correct answer.

Section 2 Test 6

A WARM-UP

Continue the sentence.

1 The clown danced even though _____

_____

2 The clown danced as if _____

_____

3 The clown danced whenever _____

_____

Add a suffix to make the word into a verb.

4 crystal_____

5 beauty_____

6 critic_____

7 identity_____

Put the letters in order to make a word.

8 g e a r u   _____

9 m y h e r   _____

10 r o o l u c   _____

B WORD WORK

Write an adverb to go with the definition.

1 _____ : with anger and aggression

2 _____ : clearly

3 _____ : more often than not

Complete the word sum.

4 **gossip** + **ing** = _____

5 **quarrel** + **ing** = _____

6 **shrub** + **ery** = _____

7 **stupid** + **ity** = _____

8 Which two words do **not** follow the spelling rule? Explain your answer.

_____ because

_____

Write a definition.

9 **metre** (in maths): _____

_____

10 **metre** (in poetry): _____

C SENTENCE WORK

Rewrite the sentence with the subordinate clause at the beginning.

1 He stepped onto the stage despite his nerves. _____

2 The door opened as she stood there weeping. _____

3 What is the effect of reordering the clauses? _____

The door opened.

Rewrite the sentence, adding plenty of detail to match the story type.

4 **school story:** _____

5 **mystery:** _____

6 **sci-fi:** _____

How does the punctuation help to make the following more effective?

Stella is now my EX-best friend – officially.

7 **capital letters:** _____

8 **dash:** _____

Em' says it's my fault (but she would say that).

9 **brackets:** _____

10 **apostrophes:** _____

Section 2 Test 7

A WARM-UP

Cross out the word that makes the phrase a cliché.
Write a more original simile.

1 as white as snow

_____

2 as quiet as a mouse

_____

3 as deep as the sea

_____

Write in full the word that the short form stands for.

4 ID _____

5 fan _____

6 ad _____

7 demo _____

Underline the hidden word.
Clue: it has at least four letters

8 s t r e g i o n t e

9 l e r p o b e y c e

10 w i c h a o s t l e

B WORD WORK

Add the same suffix to all three words.

1 grace_____   thunder_____   envy_____

2 effect_____   act_____   expense_____

3 music_____   person_____   nature_____

4 Write the name of the class of words that
you have made.

_____

5 Add a short word to complete the longer word.

com_____y   ske_____on

fat_____ing   ve_____able

6 How does this help you to spell the
words correctly?

_____

_____

Add the same word to complete both idioms.

7 in _____ pursuit; red _____ favourite

8 the _____ is on; in the _____ of the moment

9 out _____ ; make the blood run _____

10 a _____ customer; keep your _____

C SENTENCE WORK

Complete the conditional sentence.

1 The sponsored walk will go ahead on Friday unless _____

2 People would not drop litter if _____

3 Martin will be able to come, provided that _____

4 They will be here soon, so long as _____

Write a one-sentence summary of the story. Include a connective.

5 **Cinderella** _____

6 **Goldilocks** _____

7 **Robin Hood** _____

Add a semi-colon.

8 There was no choice we had to leave.

9 The house was empty nothing stirred.

10 Don't interrupt I haven't finished.

24

Section 2   Test 8

A   WARM-UP

Write a question-and-answer joke based on the homonym.

1   trunk: _____

_____

2   wave: _____

_____

3   watch: _____

_____

Add the same short word to complete both longer words.

4   des_____ation   ex_____guish

5   cour_____   man_____

6   es_____lish   s_____le

7   be_____ve   re_____f

Add the missing letters.

Clue: story types

8   m__s t__r__

9   h__m_____r

10   __d v__n_____

B   WORD WORK

Add a word to complete each compound word.

1   _____fore

2   hence_____

3   _____theless

4   _____over

5   Underline the unstressed vowels.

   t e l e g r a p h   p a r a l l e l

   m o n o g r a m   m u l t i p l y

6   Write the word root from the start of each word above.

_____

7   Why do root words help you to remember the correct spelling? _____

_____

Write a modern phrase that means the same.

8   **set forth:** _____

9   **yonder:** _____

10   **go thither:** _____

C   SENTENCE WORK

Rewrite the sentence in the passive form without mentioning the person or people responsible.

1   Jasper slew the dragon.   _____

2   The people sent a message.   _____

3   A servant had broken the mirror.   _____

4   The postman had delivered the letter.   _____

Complete the table with words and phrases used in formal and informal letters.

	formal	informal
5	domestic residence	
6		Hi!
7	in duplicate	

Why has the colon been used?

8   There are three events: the sprint, long jump and high jump. _____

9   The speech began very formally: "Ladies and gentlemen ..." _____

10   He knew he was late: it was past nine o'clock. _____

Section 2   Test 9

A   WARM-UP

The subject is **Mud**. Write sentences using each of these sound patterns.

1 **alliteration:** _____

_____

2 **a rhyming couplet:**

_____

_____

3 **onomatopoeia:** _____

_____

Underline the word that can **not** be a verb.

4 book float ring planet bat

5 pop spot safe snap bubble

6 light lead year note ferry

Solve the anagram.

7 **hatcug:** _____

8 **netils:** _____

9 **paxilen:** _____

10 **nices:** _____

B   WORD WORK

1 Add the correct prefix. **sub anti extra**

____freeze   ____dote   ____biotic

____ordinary   ____vagant

____merge   ____ordinate   ____terranean

Write the meaning of the prefix.

2 **anti:** _____

3 **extra:** _____

4 **sub:** _____

5 Add the same grapheme to all the words.

ma___inery   heada___e

s___olar   mis___ief

6 Why is this grapheme tricky?

_____

_____

Find the original meaning.

7 **nice:** _____

8 **awful:** _____

9 **terrific:** _____

10 **quick:** _____

C   SENTENCE WORK

Rewrite the sentence as three separate sentences.

1 **It was cold now that a fog had descended so the children shivered.**

_____

2 How does this change the impact? _____

3 **They raced to the door, which was locked, so there was no escape.**

_____

4 How does this change the impact? _____

Complete the verb table.

5 eat			ate	eaten
6 go	goes	going		
7 take				
8 blow				

9 Complete the sentence using fewer than 10 words: **Falling** _____

10 Complete the sentence using more than 20 words: **As Angie** _____

X There is only one correct answer.   X There is more than one correct answer.

Section 2 Test 10

A WARM-UP

Write four different sentences using these words only.

stood Jo holding the key there calmly

1 _____

_____

2 _____

_____

3 _____

_____

4 _____

_____

Write two words that follow the mnemonic.

5 I go home tonight   _____

6 I O U some   _____

Write the antonym.

7 **future** _____

8 **prefix** _____

9 **antonym** _____

10 **rhyming** _____

B WORD WORK

Write the common root and its meaning.

1 astronaut astronomer asterisk

_____

2 monorail monocle monologue

_____

Add the correct suffix. Use each suffix once only.

3 **ful ment ly**

move_____   wake_____   true_____

4 The odd one out is _____ , because

_____

5 **able ist al**

rehearse_____   notice_____   extreme_____

6 The odd one out is _____ , because _____

_____

Write a simpler word with a similar meaning.

7 **endorse:** _____

8 **pursue:** _____

9 **cease:** _____

10 **commence:** _____

C SENTENCE WORK

Why has the writer used the passive?

1 The temperature was taken every hour. _____

2 The poor man had been robbed. _____

3 The cloak had been cut to ribbons. _____

Use personification to complete the sentence.

4 The sun _____

5 The sea _____

6 The car _____

7 The river _____

Punctuate the sentence so that it sounds effective.

8 There carved into the wood was a number 1004.

9 He ran ran ran desperately he ran.

10 It was an amazing sight the spitting hissing serpent with its staring eyes and open jaws quivering in the air.

X There is only one correct answer.   X There is more than one correct answer.   **27**

Section 2　Test 11

A　WARM-UP

Complete the sentence using a metaphor or personification.

1　Daisies _____

_____

2　An aeroplane _____

_____

3　Spring _____

_____

Complete the table.

	adjective	noun	verb
4	real		
5		vision	
6			confirm

Add the missing letters.

Clue: sources of information

7　d i c _ _ _ _ n _ _ _

8　b _ b _ _ _ _ g r _ _ _ _ y

9　e n c _ _ _ _ _ p _ d _ _ _

10　_ _ _ _ s _ _ r u s

B　WORD WORK

1　Add the correct ending.　**logy　phobia　athlon**

dec_____　　bio_____　　tri_____

hydro_____　　zoo_____　　claustro_____

Draw a line to join the root to its meaning.

2　**athlon**　　　　fear of

3　**logy**　　　　contest

4　**phobia**　　　　the study of

Add the missing vowels.

5　b e n _ f _ t　　　　**6**　s e p _ r _ t e

signal　signature　signpost　unsigned

7　Underline the root.

8　Write the words in which the **g** is silent.

_____

Explain the meaning of the proverb.

9　Don't count your chickens before they are hatched. _____

_____

10　A fool and his riches are soon parted.

_____

_____

C　SENTENCE WORK

Make the sentence a conditional sentence.

1　I could borrow the bike _____

2　He would be safe _____

3　The team would score more goals _____

4　You too can be a star player _____

Identify the text type.

story,　information text,　newspaper article

5　The crops have failed for the second year.　　_____

6　The crops shrivelled in the parched ground.　　_____

7　The ground becomes so dry that no crops can grow.　　_____

Cross out the conjunction and replace it with a semi-colon.

8　Spring is nearly here so buds will soon appear on the trees.

9　They whispered quickly because there was not much time.

10　The light went out therefore she could see nothing.

X There is only one correct answer.　　X There is more than one correct answer.

Section 2   Test 12

A   WARM-UP

Complete the proverb.

1 Too many cooks _____

2 If at first you don't succeed,

_____

Write a sentence to illustrate the proverb.

3 **Proverb 1:** _____

_____

_____

4 **Proverb 2:** _____

_____

_____

Underline the word that is **not** linked by meaning.

5 bicycle binoculars biography biceps

6 decade decimal December declare

Underline the hidden word.
Clue: it has at least four letters

7 e s t a c t i c s e n

8 k i c h e n c e r d

9 m i s h a l f e r t

10 f r i e l i k e l i

B   WORD WORK

Add the missing letters.

1 e n v i r o _ m e n t

2 g o v e r _ m e n t

3 c u _ b o a r d

4 r a s _ b e r r y

5 Explain why the words above are tricky to spell.

_____

Write two words formed by adding affixes to the root word.

6 **music** _____

7 **electric** _____

8 **mobile** _____

Write a modern word or phrase that means the same.

9 **pauper:** _____

10 **coster:** _____

C   SENTENCE WORK

Complete the sentence.

1 Limping _____

2 Frightened _____

3 Leaping _____

4 Holding _____

We like skateboarding so I think a skateboard park would be great.

5 Underline the words that make this writing sound personal and informal.

6 Rewrite the sentence to make it sound impersonal.

_____

7 What is the purpose of this writing? _____

Punctuate the sentence and add capital letters where necessary.

8 She read the nameplate Amy Miles she knew the name where had she heard it

9 A word of warning if you are tempted to try this dont

10 That was when we realised there was no going back it was too late

Now complete Section 2 of the Progress chart on page 46.

Section 2 Writing task: Moving day

Task

Dan and Megan's family are moving from the city to live in the country. Megan is pleased about the move; her brother Dan is not. Write separate diary entries for Dan and Megan for the day they arrive at their new home.

Hints

Before you start:

- Consider what might have happened on moving day.

- How might Dan and Megan have felt about these events?

- Think about what Dan and Megan might write in their diaries.

As you write:

- Remember to use an informal, conversational style.

- Choose your words carefully.

- Try out phrases and sentences to see if they sound convincing.

Dan's diary	Megan's diary

Continue on a separate sheet.

Check

- When you have finished, check through your diary entries.

- Edit and proofread them.

- Make sure that everything looks and sounds right.

Section 2 Proofreading task: Tropical trees

Task
Proofread these two texts, which are in different styles.

Hints
- Check that everything is clear and sounds right.
- Check the punctuation.
- Check the spelling.
- Change anything that does not look or sound right.

Factuel   discription

Rainforist's previde a very spetial inviranment a nachural habbitat that is home to a verietty of truelly remarkible plant's and anamal's.

Whereever light reachs the forist floor egsotic ferns and herbs flurrish igh above the trees branchis form a cannopy of leafs and flowars home to milians of inseckts and anamals. The trees previde these crechures with a reguler supley of food fruits nuts seeds and pollern.

Poetic discription
Trees of dizzeing hiight tangel together forming a secrat gardin not visable from bellow brightley colured flowors entwhine the branchis with mouthes open to the insistant rain.

Ownly tiny chinks of light and the dripdroping of rain can pirce the iner darkniss of the rainforist. Here roots hang down like ropes danngling from anshient   bells.

Extra
On a separate sheet of paper, write a brief poetic piece about your garden, local park or school grounds. Choose your words carefully. Include at least one simile and one metaphor.

Section 3   Test 1

A   WARM-UP

Continue the sentence.

1 Jemma is happy as long as _____

_____

2 Jemma is happy until _____

_____

3 Jemma is happy while _____

_____

4 Jemma is happy although _____

_____

Solve the anagram.

5 **helow:** _____

6 **athtug:** _____

7 **icento:** _____

8 **rathe:** _____

Explain the derivation.

9 **hyperlink** comes from _____

_____

_____

10 **café** comes from _____

_____

B   WORD WORK

Write the correct spelling.

1 litracey   _____

2 mathmaticks   _____

3 siense   _____

Write two words that start with the prefix.

4 **mal**   _____

5 **multi** _____

6 Write the meaning of the prefix.

mal: _____

multi: _____

Write different definitions of each word.

7 **rap:** _____

8 **rap:** _____

9 **cricket:** _____

10 **cricket:** _____

C   SENTENCE WORK

Rewrite the sentence so that the information given in brackets is embedded within it.

1 The gerbil is best suited to life in the desert. (UK – popular pet) _____

_____

2 Birds of prey include hawks and owls. (hawks hunt – day; owls hunt – night) _____

_____

3 Edward Jenner pioneered vaccination. (b. 1749; a doctor) _____

_____

What techniques has the writer of this advert used to persuade the reader to buy?

Get light on your feet with Flash trainers – truly awesome ...

4 **sentence type:** _____   5 **language:** _____

6 **word play:** _____

7 **punctuation:** _____

Write a line of dialogue to open the traditional story.

8 **Red Riding Hood** _____

9 **Snow White** _____

10 **Aladdin** _____

X There is only one correct answer.   X There is more than one correct answer.

Section 3   Test 2

A   WARM-UP

Write a sentence using these words.

spell caterpillar

1 **simple sentence:** _____

2 **question:** _____

3 **compound sentence:** _____

_____

4 **complex sentence:** _____

_____

_____

Complete the words.

5 _____py → py_____

6 _____it → it_____

7 _____al → al_____

8 _____gh → gh_____

Make three words.

9 **auto tele cue gram graph**

_____

10 **med graph para ic al**

_____

B   WORD WORK

Complete the word to go with the definition.
Use a dictionary to check the spelling.

1 ant_____ : very old

2 ant_____ : collection of poems
or stories

3 ant_____ : dislike; hostility

4 ant_____ : aerial; one of the feelers
on an insect

5 These words are mixed up. Write them correctly.

webport helilung aquacam

_____

Write a more formal synonym.

6 **try** _____

7 **watch over** _____

8 **ask for** _____

9 **turn down** _____

10 **go ahead** _____

C   SENTENCE WORK

Complete the sentence.

1 Hiding _____

2 Balanced _____

3 Peering _____

4 Surprised _____

What type of text is the sentence taken from?

5 Flour is mixed with water, yeast and salt.   _____

6 Mix the yeast and salt into the flour. Then add the water.   _____

7 The salt and yeast were then added to the flour.   _____

Use brackets to add extra explanation or examples.

8 Icebergs are formed when glaciers _____ meet the sea.

9 Bread, pasta _____ and some cereals are made from wheat.

10 Different types of figurative language _____ are used to
create a mood or feeling.

Section 3 Test 3

A WARM-UP

Write an advert for Sam's new range of soups using

1 **alliteration:** _____

2 **word play:** _____

3 **a rhetorical question:** _____

_____

4 **rhyme:** _____

Write a word using these letters. The letters must be used in this order.

5 **a b c** _____

6 **f g h** _____

7 **m n o** _____

Write the prefix that can be added to all three words.

8 final colon circle _____

9 natural structure human _____

10 light wake board _____

B WORD WORK

Add the same ending to all three words.

ary ery ory

1 direct____ categ____ fact____

2 rot____ volunt____ tribut____

3 myst____ jewell____ machin____

4 Complete the word to go with the definition.

ball____ : a song or poem

ball____ : a type of dance

ball____ : a vote

Read the words you made in question 4.
Write the words that are derived from each meaning of the word **ball**. Use a dictionary to help you.

5 **ball:** a dance _____

6 **ball:** a round object _____

7 Write three words starting with the root **aero**.

_____

Underline the word in **bold** that is used correctly.

8 a weather **vein / vane / vain**

9 a ten-**story / storey** building

10 The tiger hunted its **pray / prey**.

C SENTENCE WORK

Rewrite the sentence in the passive form.

1 A sudden scream startled him. _____

2 The swirling lights dazzled her. _____

3 The man's strange clothing puzzled me. _____

4 The sound of the sea calmed Ellie's mind. _____

Add a word or phrase for emphasis.

5 This is _____ vital.

6 This creature is now _____ rare.

7 The last _____ point is safety.

Add a colon and complete the sentence.

8 There are five vowels _____

9 These are examples of conjunctions or joining words _____

10 The room was now completely empty _____

34   X There is only one correct answer.   X There is more than one correct answer.

A WARM-UP

Complete the warning using word play.

1 Be careful of lions _____

_____

2 Watch out for boars _____

_____

3 A cheetah _____

_____

Solve the anagram with a one-word answer.

4 **Wes ran:** _____

5 **Chloe coat:** _____

6 **Sid co:** _____

7 Write in the missing animal.

That's put the _____ among the pigeons.

Write three other idioms featuring the same animal.

8 _____

9 _____

10 _____

B WORD WORK

Check the spelling of the animal name.
Write the correct spelling.

1 pidgin _____

2 sqirrul _____

3 leperd _____

Use a suffix to make the noun into an adjective.

4 **triangle** _____

5 **hexagon** _____

6 **cylinder** _____

Write different definitions of each word.

7 **grate** (noun): _____

8 **grate** (verb): _____

9 **hide** (noun): _____

10 **hide** (verb): _____

C SENTENCE WORK

Reorder the sentence so that it focuses on the feelings of the character.

1 He walked on although he was scared. _____

2 They followed the others, as if in a trance. _____

3 Ed crawled into the cave despite the pain. _____

4 He stood up with a tingle of excitement. _____

5 Write three phrases that introduce one side of an argument.

_____

6 Write three phrases that introduce a different opinion.

_____

7 Write three connectives that introduce an opposing view.

_____

Add the missing commas.

8 Then there was the way she looked at me unpleasantly as if I were an insect.

9 When the beetroot is cool press it through a sieve collecting the juice in a bowl.

10 Smiling contentedly Sarah sank into the armchair glad to be home at last.

| X | There is only one correct answer. | X | There is more than one correct answer. |

35

Section 3   Test 5

A   WARM-UP

Write a sentence using these words.

goat socks

1   **active:** _____

_____

2   **passive:** _____

_____

3   **imperative:** _____

_____

Add a number to complete the word.

4   sen_____ce   6   w_____less

5   l_____ly   7   ne_____rk

Write a headline using a pun based on the homophones.

8   **main/mane:** _____

_____

9   **not/knot:** _____

_____

10 **aloud/allowed:** _____

_____

B   WORD WORK

Add the same ending to all three words. **cial tial**

1   essen_____   poten_____   torren_____

2   spe_____   artifi_____   finan_____

Add the same ending to all three words.

3   popul_____   pill_____   regul_____

4   flav_____   col_____   hum_____

Add a different root word to complete each of these space terms.

5   _____verse   _____nova   _____scope

6   _____naut   _____phere   _____ite

Write a more formal synonym to replace the word or phrase in **bold**.

7   Be **on your guard**.   _____

8   It was **okay**.   _____

9   The amount was **not enough**. _____

10 The place was **unfriendly**.   _____

C   SENTENCE WORK

Shorten the sentence by starting with the verb.

1   Although I was trembling with fear, I turned the key. Trembling _____

2   Because she was running fast, she quickly caught up. _____

3   As he gathered his strength, he climbed higher. _____

4   Owing to the fact that I was encouraged by the applause, my confidence returned.

_____

5   Underline the adjectives. **Each snowflake is individual and unique.**

6   What do the adjectives tell us about the design of snowflakes? _____

7   Underline the verbs.   **As the bulldozers advance, all wildlife flees.**

8   Why has the writer chosen these verbs? _____

Add the commas, full stops and capital letters.

9   On the doorstep Ayesha stopped she must be too early there was no sound coming from inside no music or sounds of laughter.

10 Whales are mammals not fish they are covered with skin not scales.

X There is only one correct answer.   X There is more than one correct answer.

Section 3   Test 6

A WARM-UP

Write three different sentences using these words only.

came stomping the giant over the hill

1 _____

2 _____

3 _____

Complete the words.

4 _____ hon → hon _____

5 _____ fer → fer _____

6 _____ com → com _____

7 _____ mic → mic _____

Underline the word that is wrongly spelt.

8 arguable adorable agreable

9 dissbelief disservice discourage

10 halves rooves thieves

B WORD WORK

Write the correct spelling of the library sign.

1 200 werld relijons and beleefs

_____

2 400 Inglish and forern langwidges

_____

3 600 tecknolajy, mashines, invenshuns

_____

Write two words related to the word in **bold**.

4 **public** _____

5 **memory** _____

6 **origin** _____

Add the correct word.

larva lava

7 volcanic _____

8 caterpillar _____

symbols cymbals

9 I play the _____

10 There were _____ on the map.

C SENTENCE WORK

Rewrite the sentence in the passive form to make it sound impersonal.

1 I sent a letter to the newspaper. _____

2 We will have to cancel the concert. _____

3 We provide a choice of activities. _____

4 I have taken steps to prevent this. _____

What narrative technique has the writer used to engage readers?

5 Hanif ran, Hasan ran, everyone ran. _____

6 The path divided. Which way now? _____

7 Well, what could I do? _____

Punctuate the text extract, adding capital letters if necessary.

8 Museum opening times 10.00 6.00 last admission 5.00

  Molly's cafe is open all day for snacks sandwiches rolls cakes tea and coffee

9 Fanatical about football potty about the premiership try Striker available NOW

10 Force 9 roof tiles dislodged damage to chimneys branches blown off trees

Section 3 Test 7

A WARM-UP

Continue the sentence.

1 **active sentence:** The sword _____

_____

2 **passive sentence:** The sword _____

_____

3 **complex sentence:** The sword _____

_____

Add a short word to complete the longer word.

4 g _____ tly

5 o _____ ient

6 a _____ oned

7 je _____ ery

Complete the sentence.

8 **Archaeology** is the study of

_____

9 **Etymology** is the study of _____

10 Underline the **ology** that is **not** a real word.

zoology meteorology snowology sociology

B WORD WORK

Add the missing syllables.

1 dis / _____   **Clue:** it hides who you are

2 con / _____ / _____   **Clue:** not a vowel

3 Add the same missing syllable to all three words.

gen / ____ / al av / ____ / age gen / ____ / ous

4 How does saying syllables help you to spell?

_____

Write two words related to the word in **bold**.

5 **refer** _____

6 **govern** _____

Write a definition.

7 **schooner:** _____

8 **buccaneer:** _____

9 **doubloon:** _____

10 If used in a story title, what would these words tell you about the setting?

_____

_____

C SENTENCE WORK

Complete the sentence with a statement of what might have happened.

1 If Jack had not climbed the beanstalk _____

2 If Cinderella had not lost her shoe _____

3 If Goldilocks had not run away _____

4 If the boy had not cried 'Wolf!' _____

Rewrite the sentence using more formal vocabulary.

5 We shouldn't wear jeans to school. _____

6 The centre helps old people. _____

7 People want the councillors to rethink. _____

8 We want money to make up for the mess. _____

9 Punctuate the information as **two** sentences, adding the capital letter where necessary.

On average a person in the UK uses 150 litres of water a day in parts of Africa, each person has just ten litres a day.

10 Punctuate it again as **one** sentence.

On average a person in the UK uses 150 litres of water a day in parts of Africa, each person has just ten litres a day.

X There is only one correct answer.   X There is more than one correct answer.

A WARM-UP

The subject is **Umbrellas**. Write a sentence using

1 **a rhyming couplet:**

_____

_____

2 **onomatopoeia:** _____

_____

3 **a simile:** _____

_____

Add one letter to make a different word.

4 scare → _____

5 contact → _____

6 crate → _____

Draw a line to join the word in **bold** to its language of origin.

7 **patio**   Norwegian

8 **ski**   Japanese

9 **solo**   Spanish

10 **judo**   Italian

B WORD WORK

Complete the word sum. Check the spelling carefully.

1 **humour** + ous = _____

2 **fame** + ous = _____

3 **marvel** + ous = _____

Write a definition.

4 **graphology:** _____

5 **photophobia:** _____

6 **transfigure:** _____

7 **micrometer:** _____

_____

Complete the unfinished words in these formal signs.

8 All empl_____ will be issued

with a work per_____.

9 Please en_____ that you pro_____

a contact number for use in an em_____.

10 Further details ava_____ on re_____.

C SENTENCE WORK

Rearrange the sentence so that the subject comes at the end.

1 There was a huge bull right in front of me. _____

2 There was the dog, staggering towards him, thin with hunger.

_____

3 The giant beast slowly loomed out of a thin swirling mist.

_____

A light drizzle began to fall, shrouding the street in greyness.

4 What mood has the writer created? _____

5 How has this been achieved? _____

Complete the sentence to create a sense of

6 **calm:** The water _____

7 **tension:** The darkness _____

Continue the sentence using either a comma, a dash or a colon.

8 A word of warning_____

9 Waving his fists_____

10 Now he was frightened_____

Section 3   Test 9

A   WARM-UP

A tiger has escaped from the local zoo.

Rewrite the sentence as

1 **a headline:** _____

2 **a rhyming couplet:**

_____

_____

3 **a complex sentence:** _____

_____

_____

Solve the anagram with a one-word answer.

4 **tears:** _____

5 **was here:** _____

6 **I drew:** _____

Write the day of the week that means

7 day of the Moon: _____

8 day of Saturn: _____

9 day of the god Woden: _____

10 day of the god Thor: _____

B   WORD WORK

Write the correct spelling.

1 Shoping list: lettice, marjerine, rasberrys

_____

_____

2 Matereals: construksion card, addesive

_____

3 Eqipmunt: sissors, wire striper

_____

Write two words that start with the root.

4 **cert** _____

5 **spect** _____

6 **quad** _____

Write different definitions of each word.

7 **mould** (in arts and crafts): _____

_____

8 **mould** (in science): _____

9 **scale** (in science): _____

_____

10 **scale** (in geography): _____

_____

C   SENTENCE WORK

Rewrite the sentence in the passive form, without mentioning who is responsible.

1 Man's actions force some animals to find new habitats.

_____

2 Man hunted the dodo until it became extinct. _____

3 People are cutting down large areas of forest. _____

A penguin looks like a fat little waiter in evening dress.

4 Why does the writer use this simile? _____

Write a simile of your own.

5 A hippopotamus _____

6 A diplodocus _____

7 A peacock _____

Put a tick if the sentence is correctly punctuated. Put a cross if it is not.

8 If commuters used public transport, the roads would be less crowded. ____

9 Global warming is a huge concern, experts are worried about Earth's future. ____

10 Write the incorrect sentence correctly.

_____

X There is only one correct answer.   X There is more than one correct answer.

Section 3 Test 10

A WARM-UP

The subject is **The bee**. Write

1 **an acrostic:**

_____

_____

_____

2 **a rhyming couplet:**

_____

_____

Write a word using these letters. The letters must be used in this order.

3 **c i a** _____

4 **p l c** _____

5 **p t o** _____

6 **t f c** _____

Use word play to write a name for a

7 **hairdresser:** _____

8 **fish and chip shop:** _____

9 **flower shop:** _____

10 **bakery:** _____

B WORD WORK

Add the missing letter or letters.

Clue: is it single or double?

1 re____o____end   **2** ne____e____ary

3 Write a mnemonic for one of these words.

_____

This is a made-up word. Write a definition.

4 **autoathlon:** _____

5 **triscopic:** _____

6 **phobiometer:** _____

What thou seest when thou dost wake,

Do it for thy true love take;

7 Underline the words which show that these lines were written long ago.

What do you notice about

the verbs?

8 _____

the pronouns?

9 _____

10 _____

C SENTENCE WORK

Complete the sentence.

1 If we keep the plant in the cupboard, _____

2 If we all drove electric cars, _____

3 A ban on cars in the town centre would _____

4 What is the purpose of sentences like these? _____

Rewrite the sign using more formal language.

5 Sorry if the building work caused you problems.

_____

6 You can't use your camera. _____

7 Be sure to have all your papers with you.

_____

Punctuate and continue the book blurb.

8 When Lenny the alien joins Class 6 strange things happen – _____

9 One stormy night Josh finds shelter in a deserted barn – _____

10 Marcie an orphan lives with her gran in Victorian London where she is very happy –

_____

A WARM-UP

Continue the sentence.

1 If you stand in the rain too long, _____

_____

2 If I were prime minister, _____

_____

3 If the sun forgot to rise, _____

_____

Draw a line to join the dinosaur name to its meaning.

4 megalosaurus   three horned

5 triceratops   fast plunderer

6 velociraptor   great lizard

Underline the hidden word.
Clue: it has at least four letters

7 r i s t a w a r e r t h

8 p r e t h a l s e d i t e

9 t r a c i r c l e k t l e

10 n a d g e n r e n g e r d

B WORD WORK

Cross out the words that are wrongly spelt.
Write the correct spelling.

1 His berthday is definately in Febuerry.

_____

2 He sined the holerday form for the secratery.

_____

3 I prefered the more chalangeing clime.

_____

Add the same suffix to all three words.

ous ity ess

4 lion_____   god_____   prince_____

5 hazard_____   poison_____   envy_____

6 curious_____   generous_____ possible_____

Write different definitions of each word.

7 font (in RE): _____

8 font (in IT): _____

9 colon (in science): _____

_____

10 colon (in literacy): _____

C SENTENCE WORK

Rewrite each sentence twice. First make it shorter and more effective. Then make it longer and more effective.

Then they saw that Nina had vanished.

1 shorter: _____

2 longer: _____

They ran away as fast as they could.

3 shorter: _____

4 longer: _____

5 Tick the most effective story ending.

Then I woke up. It was all a dream.   ____

We went home and had tea.   ____

Peace returned to the planet – for a little while, at least.   ____

6 Explain your choice: _____

Add a comma or a semi-colon.

7 The crowd parted he stood alone.

8 As the fog lifted the dawn began to break.

9 Racing past she grabbed the sword.

10 It was frosty I was glad of the hot drink.

X There is only one correct answer.·   X There is more than one correct answer.

A WARM-UP

Write a sentence using personification.

1 The volcano _____

2 Frost _____

3 The machine _____

aqua auto hyper

mega scope scribe vision

Make up four new words of your own, using these roots only. Then write a definition of each word.

4 _____ : _____
   _____

5 _____ : _____
   _____

6 _____ : _____
   _____

7 _____ : _____
   _____

Write a mnemonic to help you spell

8 **people:** _____

9 **length:** _____

10 **laugh:** _____

B WORD WORK

Add the missing syllables.

1 vol / ____ / ____   *Clue: unpaid worker*

2 c____ / p____ / mi____   *Clue: an agreement*

3 ap / p____ / ____ / ____ *Clue: suitable, fitting*

4 im / ____ / ____ / ____ / ____ *Clue: straightaway*

Write the word to go with the definition.
Use the root in **bold** to help you spell it.

5 _____ (noun):

   the way you **sign** your name

6 _____ (noun):

   a state of not being **active**

7 _____ (adjective):

   out of the **ordinary**

These sentences are about a dance. Underline the words we do **not** use today. Write the words that we would use instead.

8 She doth but very softly go.   _____

9 Tis not fast; tis not slow.   _____

10 Foot it featly here and there.   _____

C SENTENCE WORK

We need money to keep the animal shelter open.

Express this idea in three different ways. Start each new sentence with the given word.

1 Money _____

2 If _____

3 Unless _____

Rewrite the sentence so that it **shows** rather than **describes** the character's feelings.

4 Mum was angry.   _____

5 Ellen was scared.   _____

6 Oliver was sad.   _____

7 Mr Jacks was happy. _____

Correct the punctuation.

8 Its official Banana's are the UKs favourite fruit, we eat more of them than any other fruit.

9 Of course keeping fit, is not just for players of sport fitness is a goal for all.

10 There hidden, below, was the treasure the treasure that Jo had always dreamt of.

Now complete Section 3 of the Progress chart on page 46.

Section 3 Writing task: Proposed road development

Task

There are plans to build a new road in your area. Some local people think this is a good idea and others are against it. A meeting is to be held to discuss the issue. Write a formal notice explaining the plan and inviting people to come to the meeting.

Hints

Before you start:

- Decide on the purpose of the meeting.
- Decide what information the notice needs to contain.
- Consider the reasons why the road might be needed.
- Ask yourself, 'Why are some people for the idea?' and 'Why are some against it?'

As you write:

- Think about the style needed for this formal notice.
- Choose carefully both the words that you use and the way in which you express the ideas.

Continue on a separate sheet if you need to.

Check

- When you have finished, check through your notice.
- Edit and proofread it.
- Make sure that everything looks and sounds right.

44

Section 3 Proofreading task: Alone in a strange crowd

Task
Proofread this extract from a story.

Hints
- Check that everything is clear.
- Check the punctuation.
- Check the spelling.
- Change anything that does not look or sound right.

It was quiet incredable one minite I was in the liberey, thuming throow an old histery book, and now well now were egsactly was I? The bookshelfs had vannished, the computtors had vannished even the bilding had vannished evrything had just dissapeared I was allone in a street full of strangors.

Nerveusly, I shrunk into the shaddows awere that peeple were eying my cloths with a mixchure of curiousity and suspittion. I have to admitt, a swetshirt and geans did look a little out of plaice, everyone ellse was dressed like xtras from Oliver Twist all bussles and maggitianlike top hat's What was hapenning. Was it someones humourous little joke I felt totaly abbandoned.

In confusiun and desprate to find something or someone familier, I set off in a transelike state ownly narrowley avoidding a colision with a barrow and it's owner.

"Wotch where y goin mate the barrow boy exclamed" "Just arivved from the countery, have y he added in a qaint but not unfrendly tone.

Extra
On a separate sheet of paper, continue the dialogue that begins in the final paragraph above.
Begin with the narrator's response to the question from the barrow boy.

English Skills 5 Progress chart

Name				Class/Set	
Teacher's name				Date	

Instructions

Read the **'I can' targets** for the section you have just finished.
- Colour the circle **green** if you find it **easy** to do what is described.
- Colour the circle **orange** if you are **getting there**, but still need to work on it.
- Colour the circle **red** if you still find this a **difficult** thing to do.

If there are things that you still find difficult you can work on them in the next section or in the next book.

Writing sentences

'I can' targets	Section 1	Section 2	Section 3
I can form complex sentences, varying the position of the subordinate clause.	◯	◯	◯
I can vary sentence length for effect (e.g., short for pace).	◯	◯	◯
I can write sentences in both active and passive forms.	◯	◯	◯
I can vary sentences to match the text type, audience and purpose.	◯	◯	◯
I can form conditional sentences that imagine, predict, suppose or reason.		◯	◯
I can reorder phrases and clauses for different effects (e.g., building suspense).		◯	◯

Using punctuation

	Section 1	Section 2	Section 3
I can use punctuation to clarify meaning in complex sentences or for effect.	◯	◯	◯
I can use commas to separate parts of complex sentences (e.g., phrases, lists).	◯	◯	◯
I can use apostrophes for possession and in shortened forms.	◯	◯	◯
I can punctuate accurately direct speech and quotations.	◯	◯	◯
I can use brackets, dashes and colons within sentences.	◯	◯	◯
I can form a sentence using a semi-colon.		◯	◯

Checking grammar

	Section 1	Section 2	Section 3
I can use pronouns effectively, avoiding ambiguity.	◯	◯	◯
I can use verb tenses accurately, including those with modal verbs.	◯	◯	◯
I can use the stylistic techniques and language features of different text types.	◯	◯	◯

Understanding and choosing words

	Section 1	Section 2	Section 3
I can choose adventurous and precise words (e.g., to make implications or for special effects).	◯	◯	◯
I can use a range of connecting words and phrases in different text types.	◯	◯	◯
I can use similes, metaphors and personification, avoiding clichés.	◯	◯	◯
I can vary my writing to sound informal or formal.	◯	◯	◯
I can explain the different meanings of words in different contexts.	◯	◯	◯
I can use the stylistic techniques and language features of different texts.	◯	◯	◯
I can work out word meanings using word structure and word origin.	◯	◯	◯
I can recognise some features of language used in the past.		◯	◯

Spelling

	Section 1	Section 2	Section 3
I can build words using syllables and using my knowledge of affixes.	◯	◯	◯
I can apply spelling rules and I know the exceptions to these rules.	◯	◯	◯
I can spell unfamiliar words using my awareness of a word's derivation.	◯	◯	◯
I can use common letter strings and spelling patterns to help spell words.	◯	◯	◯
I can use a range of strategies for spelling tricky words.	◯	◯	◯
I can identify and correct common spelling errors.	◯	◯	◯